Bubble Hunt

Lisa Phenicie

Illustrated by **Taryn Baker**

Bubble Hunt

ISBN 979-8-9866349-1-3 (paperback)

Illustrations: Taryn Baker
Book Design: Carla Green, Clarity Designworks

To my daughters, Bailey and Chelsey, as they hold my heart,
were my first to truly show me the joy of bubble play,
and were the inspiration for the illustrations in this book

To the many toddlers and preschoolers, of all abilities,
who have shown me firsthand the wonder and magic of bubble play
with communication in therapy

To Shelley Vieira, a forever friend and author who inspired me
to take this dream to write a children's book and make it a reality

Wow!

Two now!

Baby,
look bubbles!

Three!

Where are bubbles?

They are on me!

Pop,
pop,
pop!

Puppy, look bubbles!

Woof,
woof,
woof!

There are four!

**Bunny,
look bubbles!**

Hop,
hop,
hop!

I want more!

Duckie, look bubbles!

Quack,
quack,
quack!

Do you see?

Who is blowing bubbles?

Come hunt with me!

Wow, bubbles so big!

Oh, bubbles so small!

Hurry, catch them

one and all!

Bubbles go up high

**Bubbles
go
down
low**

So, how do

the bubbles blow?

Now I know!

Bubbles now are all done

The bubble hunt
was so
much fun!

Time to go back in the house

No more bubbles, little mouse!

Let's Talk About Speech

The words and pictures in this book were carefully chosen and designed to give some direction into what words, gestures, and sounds could be modeled to encourage communication. Functional language development occurs in the precious time together enjoying simple repetitive words in books and combining them with real objects (bubbles, wagon, stuffed animals) and conducted in a playful manner. The little ones won't even notice that they are working on sound production, language (both understanding and expressing), non-verbal communication (pointing, reaching, showing), and social communication! While talking about the pictures and/or reading the words, feel free to be animated and act out the gestures/motions, model the animal (woof, quack) and environmental sounds (pop), move the stuffed animals to varying locations (in the wagon, on Mommy's head), encourage the imitation of the actions/words (showing big and small with hands), and blow some bubbles up high and down low! You can even expand the story to create your own hunt by hiding the animals or engage family members to blow bubbles and have your child find them. Language growth is all in the interaction and play! Enjoy the bubble fun with the whole family...young or older!

Below are examples of the carefully chosen words, signs/gestures, and sounds used in the development of this *Bubble Hunt* book.

Exclamations: Wow!, Whee!

Animal and/or Environmental Sounds: pop!, woof!, quack!

Family Members: Mommy, Daddy, Baby, Papa

Core/Action Words: look, see, do, want, more, all done, hop, catch, blow

Labels: puppy, bunny, duckie, bubbles

Descriptive words: big, small, high, low

Spatial concepts: up, down, on

Signs/Gestures: all done, more, come, big, small

Question words: What?, Where?, Who?

While reading through the book, can focus on items in the pictures and have the child identify and point to items when asked 'where" something is (e.g., Where is the mouse?, Where is the puppy). As the reader, can always state "where" the items are as well to be able to let the child know that the bunny is "in" the wagon or the baby is "on" the daddy's shoulders. Incorporate some objects along with the book and the child can place items "in" and "on" items around the house. Also can pause momentarily and see if the child will imitate the animal and environmental sounds (e.g., pop, pop, pop). Bubbles truly appeal to all children and look at all of the language that can be developed with one bubble activity. Enjoy and have fun…it's all about the play and building communication together.

About the Author

Lisa Phenicie is a wife, mother of two wonderful daughters, and a Language-Speech Pathologist. In recent years, she has had the joy of working with "littles" (students between the ages of 18 months and 5 years of age). Most of her therapy is based on productive and functional play activities to encourage speech and language growth and overall communication. It has been through this work that Lisa has been able to watch the magic of bubbles bring out excitement and wonder in children of all abilities. This is Lisa's first children's book and has been such a dream to be able to put into print something that hopefully will guide families to play in such a way that helps young learners be able to communicate and find their voice.

About the Illustrator

Taryn has always had a love for art and especially enjoyed animals while growing up. She is currently an Instructional Assistant with Special Education and hopes to pursue more illustration in the future.

Made in the USA
Las Vegas, NV
17 October 2023

79269148R00024